GREAT ADAPTATIONS

A Fantastical Collection of Scientific Poems

Author, **Tiffany Taylor**
Lead Science Advisor, **David S. Wilson**
Creative Editor, **Robert Kadar**
Editor, **Molly Muldoon**
Designer, **Troy Look**
Cover Art, **J.N. Wiedle**

For information about special discounts for bulk purchases,
please contact Breadpig, Inc. at IncredibleBulk@Breadpig.com

Taylor, Tiffany
Great Adaptations.
ISBN 978-0-9785016-7-9
Breadpig, Inc.
www.breadpig.com

First edition: October 2014
10 9 8 7 6 5 4 3 2 1

PRINTED in the United States at Lake Book Manufacturing.

Table of Contents

Dog Smarts 5
Art by **Der-Shing Helmer** with science advisor **Brian Hare**

All for One and One or All! 10
Art by **Rosemary Mosco** with science advisor **David Sloan Wilson**

How Does the Crow Know? 16
Art by **Yuko Ota** with science advisor **Anne Clark**

The Mysterious Case of the Vanishing Killifish 22
Art by **Zach Weinersmith** with science advisor **Kelly Weinersmith**

Cow Chow 28
Art by **J.N. Wiedle** with science advisor **Ben Eisenkop**

Finding the Words 34
Art by **J.N. Wiedle** with science advisor **Mark Pagel**

Better Together? 40
Art by **James Munro** with science advisor **Niels Dingemanse**

How Does Your Garden Grow? 46
Art by **Esabelle Ryngin** with science advisor **Mark Moffett**

Turning Sunshine to Supper 52
Art by **Ian McConville** with science advisor **Angela Douglas**

All In 58
Art by **Ian McConville** with science advisor **Sarah Hrdy**

Tiffany Taylor, *Author*

Dr. Tiffany Taylor is an evolutionary biologist at the University of Reading. When she is not pretending to be a grown up in the lab, Tiffany Taylor loves to read silly stories and poems about almost anything. An advocate of science communication for children, she believes stories are a magic key to open and ignite young minds – a powerful tool to inspire the next generation of scientists, who one day, might just change the way we see our world. Tiffany Taylor is an active researcher in evolutionary biology, author of *Little Changes*, and a big kid at heart.

Robert Kadar, *Creative Editor*

Robert Kadar is the founder of *This View of Life*, the first online evolutionary science magazine. He aspires to bring evolutionary thinking to a general audience. Toward this end, he wishes to fuel children's insatiable curiosity of the world with the toolkit of evolution. He believes *Great Adaptations* will excite and inspire future generations of scientists.

Dog Smarts

"But I don't wanna go to school!" whined Billy from his bed.
"I've learnt all that I'll ever learn. Can't I stay here instead?"
"No!" exclaimed his mother. "That's it! I'll count to three…"
Billy turned to his dog Max. "I wish you could go for me."

"I'm sure you're smarter than I am; I see it all the time!
With just a gesture of my hand, you know what's on my mind.
You sit and stay, you talk and fetch, roll over and play dead,
And when I'm down, I know you'll come and comfort me in bed."

"Some people think that you are dumb, because you chase your tail,
We say 'don't drink from the loo!', but still with no avail.
And I can't stop you sniffing bums, trust me I have tried,
But long ago, your ancestors had the smarts to come inside."

"They realised that us humans were softies for your stare,
with cosy beds and tasty food that we were keen to share.
And the dogs that were the kindest, that didn't growl or bark,
Were asked to stay and share our homes, safe from the cold and dark."

"Now you help in many ways, with the blind, old and infirm,
Because of your compassion and ability to learn.
And if we are in trouble, on you we can depend.
So much more than a just pet, you are my best friend."

"If I had half of your brains, I'd be the smartest boy in school.
And if I could run and catch like you, the kids would call me cool.
So, Mom, here's my conclusion, and I'm hoping you'll agree,
Max should take my place at school. He's much smarter than me."

Brian Hare

Dr. Brian Hare is an associate professor of evolutionary anthropology at Duke University in North Carolina and a member of the Center for Cognitive Neuroscience, which is a division of the Duke Institute for Brain Sciences. He received his Ph.D. from Harvard University, founded the Hominoid Psychology Research Group while at the Max Planck Institute for Evolutionary Anthropology in Leipzig, Germany, and subsequently founded the Duke Canine Cognition Center when arriving at Duke University.

About the Science:

I am an evolutionary anthropologist, which means my research tries to understand how humans have evolved to look, behave and interact with each other in our very unique way. However, about 15 years ago I started to consider how "man's best friend" fit into our complex evolutionary history, and how we might have influenced their own evolutionary story. I also work a lot with chimpanzees, and one day I noticed that they failed to read a simple hand gesture in a cognition test; I said to myself "My dog can do that!" to which the psychologist running the experiment replied "Prove it!" – and I did.

Dogs have been human's loyal companions for around 40,000 years. During this time they have evolved to become far more like human infants than their wolf ancestors. The process of dog domestication gave dogs a whole new kind of social intelligence, and today dogs are probably smarter than you think! My research tries to understand the unique ways that dogs are intelligent as a result of the special relationship they share with humans.

It is important to remember that there are many ways to measure intelligence. Just because your furry friend does not seem to understand why it's not socially acceptable to drink out of the toilet doesn't mean they aren't intelligent. I have created a special dog intelligence test that rates their empathy, communication, cunning, memory and reasoning. If you are interested in seeing how your pet pooch compares, you can find out more at *www.dognition.com*.

All for One and One for All!

From tiny beginnings, now we stand tall,
But why should our cells work together at all?
For you to survive, they must all get along,
As one they are weak but together are strong.

When life first began, each cell lived alone,
Fighting to survive, out all on their own.
In a few million years, some descendants had found,
It was better to keep a few clone mates around.

When two found each other and fused into one,
They found that together they could get more done.
By becoming inseparable, in function and form,
In time, so it was, the nucleus was born.

Many working together meant they could compete;
They could travel farther to things they could eat.
But those selfish or lazy might spoil the ride,
So there had to be something that kept them on side.

Of these groups of cells, there were a just few,
Where the number of cells just grew and grew.
From simple beginnings, now they could start,
To become more than the sum of their parts,

By dividing the labor, each cell with their role,
They all worked together for their common goal.
So natural selection saw them as one,
Cells to tissues to organs, then on to become...

A flower, a piglet, a shrimp or a bee,
A chipmunk, a stingray, a shark or a flea,
A mongoose, an ostrich, a big grizzly bear,
A slow, steady tortoise or a fast, darting hare.

And still we go further, with ants and with bees,
Who will die for each other and for their colonies.
Together they conquer, but divided they fall;
It's as much all for one, as it is one for all.

If by me helping me, it's me helping you,
And by working together we both can pull through.
By aligning our interests, then you will see,
That's multicellularity!

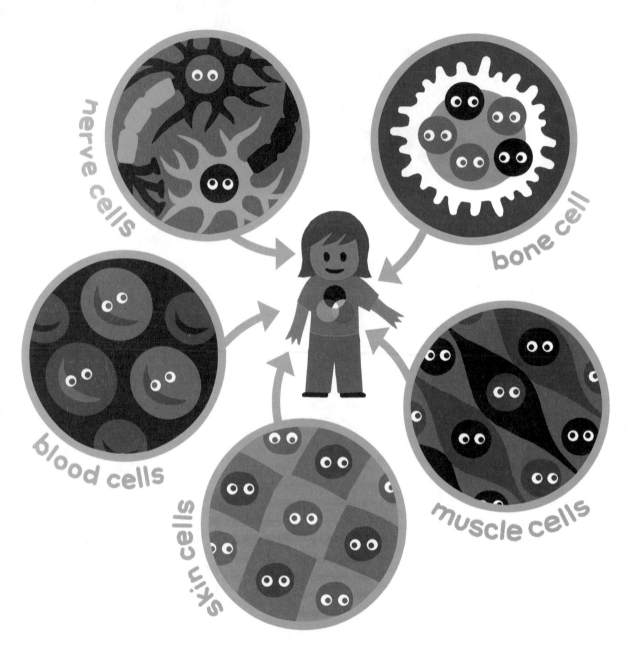

nerve cells

bone cell

blood cells

skin cells

muscle cells

David Sloan Wilson

I fell in love with nature as a kid. When I decided to be a scientist, I thought that I would have to wear a white coat and spend all my time in a laboratory. Then I discovered that I could be the kind of scientist who studies plants and animals in their natural environments—an ecologist. Even better, I learned that all creatures, from the tiniest microbe to the largest dinosaur, can be understood in terms of Darwin's theory of evolution. So I became an evolutionary ecologist and have been having fun ever since!

About the Science:

"All for One and One for All!" tells a story that was beyond Darwin's imagination. His great idea was that individuals vary, some survive and reproduce better than others and their properties are inherited by their offspring. In other words, individuals come from individuals.

The idea that was beyond Darwin's imagination was that individuals could come from groups. This idea was first proposed in the 1970s by a cell biologist named Lynn Margulis. Bacterial cells (called prokaryotic) are a lot simpler than the cells that make up you and me (called eukaryotic), which have a nucleus and other structures called organelles. Margulis proposed that eukaryotic cells did not evolve by small mutational steps from prokaryotic cells. Instead, they began as groups of prokaryotic cells that evolved to be so cooperative that the group became an organism in its own right. At first, the idea was ridiculed but by now, it has become as well established as any scientific fact.

We also know that other transitions from groups to individuals have occurred during the history of life. Life itself might have begun as groups of cooperative molecular interactions. The first cells were groups of genes and multi-cellular organisms are groups of single eukaryotic cells. Even the ant colonies described in Mark Moffett's story "How Does Your Garden Grow?" and the human groups described in Sarah Hrdy's story "Better Together" qualify as organisms to the extent that their members work together to achieve common goals. The message of my story is that the concepts of "individual" and "society" have become thoroughly entwined.

How Does the Crow Know?

In downtown Manhattan lived two common creatures,
No remarkable appearance or discernable features.
Amongst the hustle and bustle, two birds sat up high,
Watching the world as it went rushing by.

To survive in the city takes courage and tact,
To rely on your friends and to quickly react,
To strike opportunity when it comes into view,
And resist when it's just too good to be true.

Starlings and crows lived in neighboring trees,
But in so many ways they were like chalk and cheese.
Starling and friends rushed in without care,
While the crows were inquisitive and keenly aware.

"Look there!" said a starling. "I spy something to eat,
Those crumbs by the dustbin will make a fine treat."
"Oh, Starling," said a crow, "but there's one caveat:
Those dustbins are home to the neighborhood cat."

"Pfft!" said the starling, and flew to his prize,
But a crash from the dustbin came as no surprise
To the wily young crow who was looking in.
"I told you so!" he said with a smug grin.

"How did you know?" said Starling irate.
"How could you possibly anticipate
What might befall a small starling like me?
Mind-reading or a mystical ability?"

"Look there!" said Crow. "It's the neighborhood cat.
He sits by the dustbins waiting for a rat,
And that shiny red car, by the grocery store,
I'm sure I've seen it parked there before.

And that lady sitting on the bench over there,
She always offers her lunches to share.
Now look at your starlings, all diving straight in.
They've got no idea at what lies within!

You must assume that one will react
Quickly enough that you all can fall back.
Assuming is brave; there's a cost if you lose,
I'd rather know all the risks in my moves.

So I watch very closely and I sit and I wait,
While another crow goes to investigate,
And I keep a look out, ready to call,
Should there be danger about to befall.
And if all is well and the risk is minute,
Then, only then, will they plunder their loot.

It's not out of kindness or loving behavior;
I know they'll stay close to return the favor.
And so, little starling, you ask how I know?
'Cause sometimes it pays to take in the show."

"Well" said Starling, "while your reasoning's good,
It's not going to help me get any food;
So if you'd be so kind, please show me the way,
To the lady who gives her lunches away."

Anne Clark

I grew up in rural Maryland, USA, watching, catching, or keeping animals of all kinds: dogs, cats, spiders, snakes and skunks. A book about evolution and the travels and ideas of Charles Darwin introduced me to evolutionary theory when I was 12. At the University of Chicago, I became an evolutionary biologist specializing in behavioral ecology, how the behavior of animals evolves in relation to the environments where they live. My particular interest has always been social behavior. I have studied the social world of bushbabies (a kind of nocturnal primate) and harvester termites, the parental behavior of budgerigars and red-winged blackbirds, and for almost 15 years, the socially complex and changing world of American crows. I also teach college courses in animal behavior and related topics (like "behavior and disease"!) at Binghamton University where I am an associate professor in the Department of Biological Sciences.

About the Science:

Have you ever wondered why some animals live in our cities and others do not? What does an animal need to move in with us, to adapt to a noisy, well-lit life close to humans?

Cities provide new foods and places to live, so successful species can't be too picky about where they make their homes or what kind of food they eat; they need to be "generalists." But cities also have new problems and dangers—machinery, dogs and cats, food in dangerous places, and people themselves. Being able to learn by experience what is good, what to avoid, what to watch, and what to ignore can mean success. Indeed, many city-living animals have big brains and good learning abilities.

American crows, like the one in the poem, are generalists. They eat things from insects, to grains, to mice, to hamburger buns. And, like other species in the crow family, they are big-brained, curious, and quick learners. But two other traits keep them out of trouble: they are cautious about approaching anything new and they live in groups and watch out for each other. A crow in a tree will tell a crow on the ground when it sees danger. While real crows can't discuss their strategy, they are more scared of new things than starlings and have an alarm system that starlings don't.

The Mysterious Case of the Vanishing Killifish

Down in the depths of a big blue lagoon, a shoal of young killifish play,
Hidden in shadows, away from sharp beaks and safe from falling as prey.
"Don't go too far!" comes a voice from the bank. "There's something out there in the blue!"
"Fish seem to vanish from this here lagoon, and you don't want it happening to you!"

"Hi, Mrs. Fundulus. Yes, yes, we know," replied all fishes all in chorus.
"Don't worry about us. We'll keep a look out and scram if we see it come for us."
Mrs. Fundulus was right. There was something lurking but it didn't look scary at all:
No big sharp teeth or menacing glare; in fact, it was incredibly small.

These small, creepy flukes, as they are called, start out their life a bit glum,
Still as an egg, before they can hatch, they're pooped out through a bird's bum.
The eggs are ingested by an unwitting snail who is keen on a bit of bird poo,
And if a diet like that wasn't unlucky enough, the flukes then hatch in them too!

Now little more than a fluke factory, flukes emerge from the snail day by day,
And free at last, they prowl the lagoon for a new victim to swim their way.
They lurk in the waters swimming to and fro, as now all they can do is wait.
But when a shadow suggests that a fish is nearby, the unlucky host seals its fate.

Now the small flukes, they swim loop the loops, hoping opportunity calls,
And a young killifish soon crosses their path and they latch on with their suckered jaws.
But now these foul flukes, they have a dilemma, for the fish is not their last stop.
They must find their way back into a bird from which their eggs can then plop.

There's a chance that a bird might just fly by but the flukes do not like to wait,
So they put into motion their devious trick so it isn't just left up to fate.
Like out of a nightmare, the flukes crawl inside and navigate up to the brain.
Masters of tricks and of mind-control, they make the fish act for their gain.

The fish will return still none the wiser and carry along as before,
Unaware he is no longer just one, but carries in him many more.
But here's where the flukes show what they can do, true puppet masters with skill,
The fish starts to twitch and wriggle and tic, and the fish loses his own free will.

He thrashes and flashes his silvery scales, for all in the heavens to see.
He swims near the surface, still jerking around, where it's just not safe to be.
And sooner or later, a hungry bird sees the fish from the shore
And quick as flash, he gobbles his catch and the young killifish is no more.

So this a story of David and Goliath, although admittedly it may seem unkind.
But it's amazing to think that a small little fluke has the power to rule giants' minds.
The mysterious case of the vanishing fish is not one of magic at all,
But a monster's a monster, whatever its size, even incredibly small.

Kelly Weinersmith

Kelly Weinersmith is a Ph.D. student at The University of California Davis in the lab of Dr. Andrew Sih. She studies parasite manipulation of host phenotype and is currently focusing on four problems:

1. How does host personality change following infection?
2. Through which mechanisms do parasites manipulate host behavior?
3. What are the ecological implications of parasite manipulation of host behavior?
4. What are the evolutionary implications of parasite manipulation of host behavior?

She received funding from the National Science Foundation for her dissertation research, and she was an American Association of University Women Dissertation Fellow. You can learn more about Kelly's research at *www.Weinersmith.com.*

About the Science:

We are all familiar with how parasites change our behavior by making us feel sick. I, for one, spend more time in bed, watch more bad TV shows, and eat a lot more ice cream when I'm sick. But parasites can change a host's behavior in ways that are much more subtle and directly benefit the parasite. For example, Dr. Kevin Lafferty and Kimo Morris discovered that the brain-infecting parasite *Euhaplorchis californiensis* (the fluke mentioned in the story) can make its host, the California killifish (*Fundulus parvipinnis*), behave conspicuously and increase its chances of being eaten by the next host in the parasite's life cycle – a bird. Conspicuous behaviors include quick jerks forward and flashing the fish's silvery belly up towards the sun. These behaviors appear to draw the attention of fish-eating birds. After the fish has been eaten, the parasites live and breed in the bird's gut. My research explores how infection by the parasite influences the killifish's "personality" by changing chemical signals in the brain and how personality differences in killifish might increase their chances of becoming infected by a parasite in the first place.

My colleague Alejandra Jaramillo perhaps described the killifish's movement best when she said that the killifish appear to be dancing through the water rather than swimming through it. I'm always amazed when I stand on the banks of an estuary in Southern California and watch a school of infected killifish swim by. The flashes of light as they flip upside down are dazzling.

Cow Chow

This cow is Berry. She's nothing unique.

She won't fetch a ball, won't juggle or speak.

But there are two things she likes to do:

One is to eat and one is to poo.

"Boring!" you say, "I can do that too!"

"This is 'Great Adaptations', what's great about poo?"

It's not just the poo, but it's what's packed inside,

It's what's needed to help all living things thrive

...nitrogen

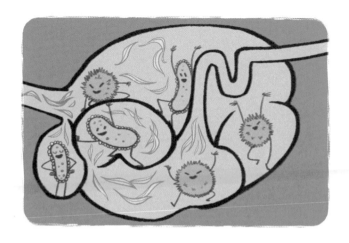

This cow is Berry. She's not big or tough,
But for all of her eating, one tum's not enough.
Look deep inside, you'll find one, two, three, four!
Teeming with types of bacteria galore.
"Why?" you might say, "would she need more than one?
Why have so many to get the job done?
What's in her food that's worth so much clout?
And why do the bacteria need to help out?"

…nitrogen

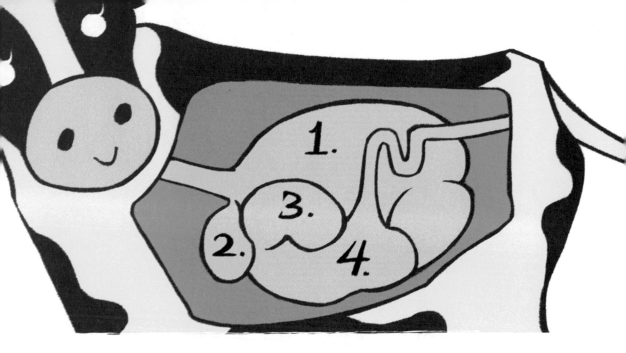

This cow is Berry. I think she's first class,
In her churning innards she transforms the grass
To the thing that makes proteins and all DNA,
That keeps our cells living and working each day.
"So, getting at nitrogen seems pretty tough,
But Berry's manure is full of the stuff!
She's got chewing power and time to invest
And an army of microbes to help her digest"

...nitrogen

This cow is Berry. I think she's the best.
Without ever complaining she helps out the rest.
But 'doing' her part doesn't take much 'do',
Just a chew and poo in her field with a moo.
"So what happens now, where does it go?"
To all living things, to help their cells grow.
Then back to the air, into plants and then so,
Its back to the start of the cycle we go.

...nitrogen

This cow is Berry. She's my best friend.

Ben Eisenkop

Ben Eisenkop is an ecosystem ecologist working on his doctorate at Binghamton University who investigates patterns of nitrogen biogeochemistry in relation to the behaviors of various animals including the American crow (*Corvus brachyrhynchos*) and teaches as a graduate instructor. He is also the person behind the alias "Unidan" on the news and link aggregator website *Reddit.com*, where he has reached millions of users by delivering "micro-lectures" on various biological topics and produced ecology-themed videos on YouTube. He has been featured on *Mashable.com*, *The Daily Dot* and *MentalFloss.com* for his scientific writing, and has recently garnered praise for his unconventional methods of funding science projects.

About the Science:

When I started my doctoral work with the incredible Dr. Weixing Zhu on nitrogen biogeochemistry, he stressed the importance of understanding ecosystems as a whole, figuring out the system in its entirety and attempting to cover every angle as best as you could. This, of course, is a task easier said than done! I try to describe my work to others as sort of being an "accountant for the environment." Some things come in, they may get changed, and different quantities may leave. It is our job to understand these "transactions" and trace their impacts.

We began a collaboration with Dr. Clark, another science advisor on this book, to apply this "accounting" to her study population of American crows (*Corvus brachyrhynchos*), which has since branched into studying other animals including cattle. We study the animal's behavioral patterns: where they go, how often they reside in an area, and what they leave behind or take with them. For example, with the cattle, I worked with my wonderful labmate Rebecca Heintzman to find out how much plant biomass cattle were removing through grazing, what changes the cattle (and their waste) were effecting in the soil and what the consequences of this would be for the plant communities.

We hope that this research can help us evaluate the effect of animals on the world around us through the creation of nutrient "hot spots" in waterways, the soil and air. In addition to the research conducted, we also made the valuable discovery that grazing exclosure plots with tall grasses can be used as makeshift hiding spots in case you are being chased by an errant bull.

Finding the Words

What's in a word? It's just a few sounds, a "ma" and a "ma", nothing more,
But the moment those sounds came out of my mouth, my mom almost fell to the floor.
She ran around the house, swirling about, brimming and laughing with joy.
"Oh my darling that's right, I'm your 'ma-ma' alright, and you are my sweet baby boy".

But what, I wondered, is so special about words? The animals get by okay.
They sing and they squawk, they bark or they snort, when they have got something to say.
I don't see the need for the all of the fuss. Those words upon words get confusing.
We can cry if it's sad, and smile if it's good, and laugh if we find it amusing.

"But think," said my mom, "if you were a lion, you'd roar to showoff your might.
And any young lion wandering by would think that you wanted to fight.
But with words you could talk and tell the young lion, 'My friend, I'm terribly sorry.
Please do excuse me. I'm just being noisy. There really is no need to worry.'"

"So," then I thought, "if I were a bird, I'd sing for a female to hear,
And I'd have to sing every song that I knew, to try and impress her sweet ear.
But with words I'd tell her 'Darling, I'll provide, and you'd be wise to pick me,
'Cause I have the strength, the smarts, and the will to give you a big family.'"

"And if I were a chimp out looking for food and I found a nut, big and tasty,

Yet try as I might, the nut wouldn't crack, so I became bothered and hasty,

If I found the words I'd say, 'My good fellow! Could you tell me what I should do?'

Instead I'm left nut-less, while my chatty friends enjoy not just one nut but two!"

"Now I can see these words upon words is a way in which knowledge is taught.

We can converse and share our ideas and describe our personal thoughts."

So forgive your poor mother if she overreacts but in truth you're pretty unique

For of all of the animals, in all of the world, we're the ones that learned how to speak.

Mark Pagel

Mark Pagel is an evolutionary theorist with current interests in anthropology as well as human social and language evolution. He is Professor of Evolutionary Biology at Reading University and a Fellow of the Royal Society. His co-authored book on comparative methods in evolutionary biology is standard reading in the field, and he is Editor-in-Chief of the award winning Oxford Encyclopedia of Evolution. His many contributions to leading scientific journals range from studies of language evolution and cultural adaptation, to speciation, punctuational evolution and primate mating systems.

About the Science:

I am a scientist who tries to understand why animals, especially humans, behave in the ways that they do and why they take the forms that they do. For instance, why do most monkeys live in groups and why do some of them have long tails? Why do other animals – like leopards and grizzly bears – live mostly by themselves? When it comes to humans, there are many more questions to answer. Why are humans the only animals that speak to each other using a language, and in complete sentences? Why have humans lost all of their fur? That is, did it ever occur to you that under our clothes we are naked? The other mammals – animals like ourselves – are not naked; they still have their fur. Scientists like me believe that we can explain all of these features of animals as 'adaptations'; that is, things that make it more likely that the animal will survive and prosper. So, one reason why humans might have lost their fur is that we learned how to make clothes and so we no longer needed fur. The other animals cannot do this so they need their fur to survive in the cold or through the night.

Better Together?

In a big old oak forest, one tree was the best
Where all of the great tits wanted to nest.
But manners and patience, they weren't enough:
If you wanted this nest site, you had to get tough.

For a family of great tits, life appeared sweet.
They had all they wanted and all they could eat.
But their opulent lifestyle came at a price,
For their father was known for not being nice

He'd bully the neighbors to protect his nest,
Took what he wanted and fought for the rest.
But too busy fighting, he was never at home,
And the mother was left to parent alone.

Raising twelve chicks wasn't easy at all,
For no matter what, they just wanted more.
Spoilt, ungrateful, she still did her best,
But their riches could not buy a contented nest.

Nearby in a shrub was a family of five,
Who had to work hard if they hoped to survive.
The father was quiet, pleasant and shy,
And did what he could to help them get by.

He wouldn't waste time with squabbles and fights,
But did what he could to get home for the night.
Looking after his chicks and helping out mom,
Because two working together is better than one!

In no time at all, the chicks were all grown,
And left to make nests for families of their own.
Each of the chicks behaved just like their dad,
But who could've known that things would get bad?

This year the winter was bitterly cold,
And little was gained from being thuggish and bold.
Better were those who made more time for caring,
Less time for fighting and more time for sharing.

After the winter, the frost started to thaw,
And the bullies were quieter than they'd been before.
But those shy and meek fared better together,
And the tables were turned with a change of the weather.

As spring brought the flowers and creatures alive,
It was clear that not all of the birds had survived.
So the shy little great tit ran out in dismay,
To see if his fledglings had all done okay.

Frantically flapping between every tree,
He counted his offspring and was happy to see,
That within each nest, snuggled up warm,
Was his son or his daughter, with eggs to be born.

He stopped when he noticed a hot headed bird,
Looking sad and deflated, and without saying a word,
He knew that his fledglings had not made it through.
So he went to his friend to see what he could do.

Nervous and shaking, with chattering beak,
He plucked up the courage, and started to speak,
"I'm sorry old friend, tell me are you alright?"
To which the bully replied, "D'you wanna fight?"

Niels Dingemanse

Niels Dingemanse studies the behavioral ecology of variation in personality and behavioral flexibility. He is an Associate Professor in behavioral Ecology at the Ludwig Maximilians University of Munich and Research Group Leader at the Max Planck Institute for Ornithology, Seewiesen, Germany. His pioneering work on wild birds (great tits), fish (stickleback) and insects (crickets) at the cross-road of quantitative genetics, statistics, and evolutionary ecology, has greatly stimulated the development of animal personality research as a hot topic of current research in behavioral ecology.

About the Science:

A few weeks ago, we expanded our family with two kittens: a brother and sister from the same litter. When we opened the cardboard box back home, one jumped out and immediately explored. We named her "My", because she reminded us of "Little My" from the *Moomin* books by Tove Jansson. Her brother (Mo), in contrast, stayed behind, eventually exploring the house in time – though much more carefully.

We all know that cats and dogs differ in their 'animal personality,' but why are there different types? My work with birds has shown that personality can affect survival. Aggressive types can do very well, bullying others and getting what they want. But they tend to 'live fast and die young' and are not particularly attentive parents compared to timid or shy individuals. These pros and cons probably lead to different types of birds producing the same amount of grandchildren – both types achieve the same in different ways and do equally well.

Interestingly, personality is not something that we can predict based on how an animal looks. The same is true for our two cats My and Mo, who are so alike that we decided to mark them: one with a red and the other with a white collar. We do the same with the birds, who are all 'ringed' with distinctive color bands around their legs, so we can track them from birth to death. There is much that we have learned about how personality matters in their lives and much remains to be discovered.

How Does Your Garden Grow?

From tadpole to frog, Jim watched from his log,
Mystified by what he saw:
Ants keen to please, with gifts of green leaves,
Entered their nest by the score,
"Tell me dear ant, 'cause I surely can't,
Your efforts seem against odds.
Do you eat all this green as a favourite cuisine?
Or are they a gift to ant Gods?"

Too busy to rest, an ant yelled in protest,
"I don't have time for your question!
Our garden of food feeds us and our brood,
With a little help from ingestion."
Jim was unsure, more confused than before,
"Garden?!" he thought in reply.
More curious than ever, Jim was on an endeavour
To find out Who, What, Where and Why.

Back on his log, Jim watched the ants slog,

And yelled to an ant in the queue,

"I really must know, how does your garden grow?

And what is it that you all do?

Each day you all march, up and out from the dark,

One after one in a row.

What goes on beneath? What's the fate of your leaf?

How does your garden grow?!"

The ant's words were brief, keen to tend to her leaf,

"Our garden's not what you suggest.

It's not what is green that's our favourite cuisine,

But what's lurking down in the nest.

It is alive, and for it to survive,

We must all do our share.

For it is a fungus that lives down among us,

That requires our nurture and care."

The ant's work resumed and Jim's thoughts were consumed,
So he stopped one more ant in her tracks,
"Begging your pardon, but regarding your garden,
Can you please give me some facts?
Must you prune and weed to get what you need?
And how can it grow without sun?
And I know you're in haste, but I'm curious to taste
Your fungus if I could find some."

"We are gardeners, it's true, but there's more that we do,
We are farmers that tend to our crop.
We farm day and night to make our food grow right,
And a worker ant's jobs never stop.
By the eye of our queen, we keep our crop clean,
In case of invader attack,
Foreign fungus and bacteria would make our crop inferior,
And we have evolved to fight back."

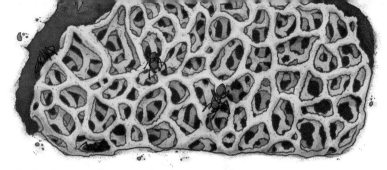

"The leaves that we feed means our crop does not need
Energy from the sun's ray,
And with chewed leaves on top to feed our growing crop,
Together we both get our way.
The fungus and ant need each other and can't
do without each to survive.
So in the end, we've come to depend
On the other to keep us alive."

"So you will not locate fungus for your plate,
The same that we feast on below,
Because we grew together, now inseparable forever,
That's how we make ant gardens grow."
Ant went back to her graft, and Jim sat and laughed.
"Well I never!", he yelled in disbelief.
"What a clever feat, to farm what you eat!"
As the ant disappeared with her leaf.

Mark Moffett

Biologist and explorer Mark W. Moffett, 'the Indiana Jones of entomology,' is a research associate at the National Museum of Natural History (Smithsonian Institution) who received his doctorate from the poet laureate of conservation biology, Edward O. Wilson at Harvard. Dr. Moffett has received the Explorers Club's Lowell Thomas Award, the Distinguished Explorer Award from the Roy Chapman Andrews Society, Yale University's Poynter Fellowship for Journalism, Harvard's Bowdoin Prize for writing, and five of his images appear in the special National Geographic publication, *100 Best Wildlife Pictures*. Among his many adventures, Moffett has climbed the world's tallest tree, descended into sinkholes a quarter mile deep to find new frog species, and placed a scorpion on Conan O'Brien's face. He has been a frequent guest of the Colbert Report. Dr. Moffett is author of *Adventures Among Ants: A Global Safari with a Cast of Trillions*, and *The High Frontier: Exploring the Tropical Rainforest Canopy*.

About the Science:

I have been self-employed ever since finishing my Ph.D., using my income from writing and photography to cover my expenses for research projects in the subjects I love — ecology and animal behavior. (Saving for retirement has never been a strong suit!) When asked by a radio show host why I did not have a job in academics, I told him, "I [didn't] do meetings." My academic friends have ribbed me for saying this! Still, I grew up on the books of 19th century explorers like the self-funded biologist Alfred R. Wallace, so it is a source of astonishment that I have managed to follow in their footsteps in today's world of specialists. The two research areas that most intrigue me are the physical structure of ecosystems such as forests — how species fit together in space — and the social behavior of ants and other animals. Tiffany's poem concerns agriculture in the leafcutter ants, a story I describe in my book *Adventures Among Ants*; as it turns out agriculture among the ants evolved in much the way as the domestication of plants such as corn or apples by humans. The frog in her poem is a poison dart frog, some of which hang around leafcutter ant nests, for reasons I don't know.

Turning Sunshine to Supper

Turning sunshine to supper may seem pretty neat,
Without moving a muscle you can conjure a treat.
So what's on the menu? The same as before,
Sunshine will boost your low energy store.

Look all around you and down at your feet.
How do the plants get what they need to eat?
With no mouth or belly, they get the job done.
When they're feeling hungry, they look to the sun.

Like big dinner plates, the leaves catch the rays.
They gobble up sunshine that passes their way.
Turning the light into sugars and so,
They find all the energy they need to grow!

Could we do the same, would it really matter?

Would sunbathing ladies get fatter and fatter?

And instead of cornflakes, when we rise from our bed,

Could we turn our face to the sunshine instead?

But alas, we cannot, and if you're wondering why,

Our bodies are thick with stuff packed inside.

In order to get what we need from the sun,

We'd have to be so skinny that we couldn't have fun.

No football, no skateboard, you'd break into two!

No dancing or skating, in fact, all you'd do,

Is sit in the sunshine, all day, getting fed,

Just like all the plants in their flower beds.

But some clever creatures can get energy,
From a pact with wee critters you can't even see.
Some tiny microbes, ever since life begun,
Have been getting their energy from rays of the sun.

The skin of these creatures is incredibly thin,
Such an inviting place for microbes to live in.
For shelter and food, they give in return,
Energy that the creatures have earned.

They live in the shallows, close to the shore,
Since long before the first dinosaur.
Sponges and corals make a great microbe inn,
A penthouse suite lies just under their skin!

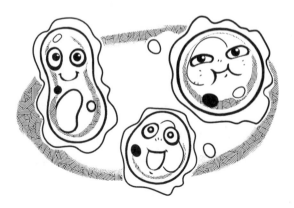

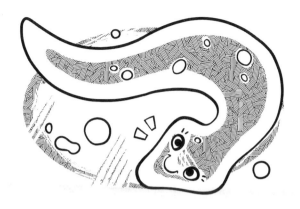

Flatworms look crazy, with colours galore,
Squashed flat like a leaf so they can catch more
Of the rays from the sun, so their microbe team
Can turn it into some flatworm cuisine.

By working together both parties can win,
A meal or a sheltered home to live in,
And so on each other they've come to depend,
And now they're inseparable, the closest of friends.

We may think we're clever with our writing and reading,
But think of the effort we go to for feeding!
We invest endless energy and oodles of time,
When these simplest of creatures can eat the sunshine.

Angela Douglas

Dr. Angela E. Douglas is the Daljit S. and Elaine Sarkaria Professor of Insect Physiology and Toxicology at Cornell University. She received a BA in Zoology from Oxford University in 1978 and Ph.D. from Aberdeen University, UK in 1981. In 1986, Angela was awarded a 10-year Royal Society Research Fellowship during which she developed a research program on insect nutritional physiology of phloem-feeding insects. Following the fellowship, Angela was a faculty member at the University of York (UK) where she was promoted to a Personal Professorial Chair in 2003 and was awarded a BBSRC Research Fellowship in 2005. She took up her current position at Cornell University in 2008. In addition to research publications and scientific reviews, Angela has authored books, including *The Symbiotic Habit* (2010), and the 5th edition of R.F. Chapman's *Insect Structure and Function* co-edited with Stephen Simpson (2013).

About the Science:

My team and I are interested in how animals interact with beneficial ("friendly") microorganisms. Animals provide a habitat for microbes and need these microbes for growth, reproduction and good health. We are especially interested in how the microbes contribute to animal nutrition and we want to solve the big puzzle of why these microbes provide the animal with nutrients, instead of keeping these nutrients to support their own growth.

Our research is motivated mostly by curiosity but it is also useful. We study plant sap-feeding insects that damage crop plants directly and by transmission of devastating plant viral diseases. These insects, including aphids, whiteflies, planthoppers and leafhoppers, depend totally on microbes in their tissues that provide essential amino acids, nutrients in short supply in the plant sap diet. We are investigating nutrient exchange between the bacteria and insect cells to identify molecular processes that can be targeted by novel control strategies specific to these interactions. We are also studying the relationship between fruit flies (*Drosophila melanogaster*) and their gut bacteria as a model for the gut microbes that are so critically important for human health. We are investigating how perturbation of the gut microbes make the fruit flies fat, even though they don't overeat and are finding that this problem depends critically on the genetic make-up of the fly. Interestingly, many of the fly genes that control the interaction between microbes and obesity in the flies are also found in people.

All In.

We are obviously different from the other apes we see,
So what is it that makes you you, and what then makes me me?
It's rooted in our history but it's something we still do,
It's caring how you think and feel, and knowing you do too.

I see when you're unhappy and I understand your pain,
You can see when I'm upset and feel it just the same.
But if there's some way I can help and stop you feeling blue,
I can share your happiness and this will help me too.

This willingness to help friends out is valuable to some,
Especially to my family and my tired brand-new mum,
Because if times are very hard, there are those happy to share,
To give me food and keep me safe, with tender loving care

My grandmother makes me laugh with tickles head to toe,
And my father teaches me the things I need to know.
My brother and my sister will keep me warm and fed,
Until its time to say "goodnight" and I'm tucked up in bed.

With so many hands to help, I can take my time to grow,
Time to learn what's safe to touch and when to stop and go.
Time to learn how to behave and cope with what life brings,
Time to understand my world and all its wondrous things.

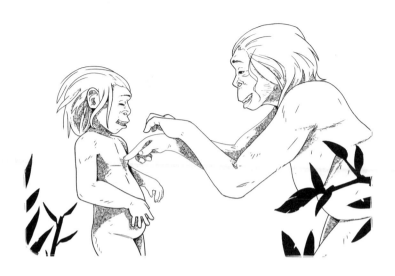

My mother trusts those in her group and so she can be sure,
That I know I'm safe and loved, sheltered and secure.
And so, in time, our family grows, and soon enough I'll be
Watching out for others and children younger than me.

We're different from the other apes in how we understand;
We share each other's feelings and we lend a helping hand.
You may only just be one, but it's important that you know,
Others help you on the way to where you want to go.

Sarah Hrdy

Anthropologist Sarah Hrdy is professor emerita at the University of California, Davis. She has been elected to the National Academy of Sciences, the American Academy of Arts and Sciences, the California Academy of Sciences and the American Philosophical Society. Her books include *The Langurs of Abu: Female and Male Strategies of Reproduction*; *The Woman that Never Evolved*; *Mother Nature: A history of mothers, infants and natural selection* and *Mothers and Others: The evolutionary origins of mutual understanding*, an exploration of the psychological implications of humankind's long legacy of shared child-rearing which was awarded both the School of Advanced Research's Staley Prize and Anthropology's Howells Prize. She also received the NAS award for Scientific Reviewing.

About the Science:

Just as Charles Darwin thought, humans descended from a line of African apes. These upright, bipedal apes known as hominins lived at a time when Africa's climate was changing. This meant diets had to change, too. Hominins scavenged and hunted meat, gathered fruits and nuts, and dug out potato-like tubers from underground. If lucky, someone located a bee hive and all enjoyed their favorite food — honey.

It took strength and special skills to locate and kill prey or crack open hard-shelled nuts. Youngsters needed someone to help provision and keep them safe from stinging insects, prowling leopards, hyenas, lions and wild dogs. Since mothers needed both hands for daily tasks, allomothers – the father and group members other than the mother – often helped to care and provide for them.

Children who grew up depending on allomothers as well as mothers learned to read intentions of caregivers and behave so as to appeal to them. Youngsters adept at ingratiating themselves had a better chance of being fed and cared for. Multiple provisioners helped children survive seasons of scarcity. Their input provided children the luxury of growing up slowly without starving and with time to learn new skills, including how to behave towards others. Over generations, multiple providers meant that food was more reliable. More energy also fueled the growth of bigger brains. The outcome was ancestral humans: more intelligent than other apes, but also more interested in what others were thinking and feeling and more eager to cooperate.

A Special Thanks to these individuals that helped make this project possible...

Aaria Reddy • Abigail and Cameron Dixon • Ada and Nicolai Berns • Aideen Hamill • Alec Ramsay • Alex Brown • Alexa & Mackenzie Alexander Bjorne • Alexander Frazer • Alexandra & Erik • Alexandra Echandi • Alexandra Golden • Amelia Ferrie • Andrea & Kurtis Broeders Andrea Woo • Andrew Doyle • Andrew Harton • Andrew J. Gnemi • Andrew J. Rowe • Andrew Schmuhl • Ann Mansker • Anonymous Anonymous • Ash F Ponders • Ashley E Beranek • Aunt Lorri • Axelle Dumas • Barry Jackson • Beatrix M. • BigFish • Brannon Moore Brenden Gallegly • Britt Koskella • Bueno &Lobl Families • C. Murtland • C.S. Onodera • Cameron Rapoza • Cat & Sam • Charles Kressbach Charles W. Salts • Christian Moestrup Jessen • Christy Filipich • Cindy and Mike Gelpi • Cindy W • Colin Griffiths • Dan & Adrian Dan and Becky Geary • Dan and Joanna Milano • Dan Menard • Dan Murray • Danzig Todd Heintz • David, Juli, Lyla and Cooper Drake de Dingemannen • Deborah J. Springer • Dr Caitlin Kight • Dr.Thomas Lee • Drake Dwornik • Dunderwood • Ed and Piper Levy Elizabeth Young • Eloise Ida Lopez • Elsie Paige Thompson • Emily and Arianna Fortner • Emma and Violet Shelley • Erin & Thorne Lawler Eris D. R. Green • Ethan Halaby • Evelyn and Joe • Fable Family • Fernando Mendoza-Alanis • Freyja Lesink • Geoff Cameron Hadassah Head • Hal • Harry Ray • Hayley Louise Smith • Heather, Michael, Evelyn, Amalia and Alexander Lerner • Hebenstreit Family Hirdhe, Keerith, Benunthi, Sonal and Manpreet Singh • Ian Skinnari • Isabel & Ivy Wilson • Israel Lidsky • J. Conklin • Jackson Rose Jade, Bradley and Raona Jeffers • James • James Tilley • Jamie Little, Nathan and Phinian Pflanz • Jeanne Garcia • Jeffrey & Martina Levy Jennifer Campbell-Smith & Zachary Smith • Jenny Reed • Jerawat • Jeremy • Jeremy Mosuela Higley • Jeremy Rishel • Jes Sloan, MD Jessica Spotts • Joanna Bryson • Joe Shelby • John Bradshaw • John, Michelle, and Morgan Grotts • Jonesbergs • Joni Friedrich • Jordan Werme Josh Wilson • Joshua Shammay • Judah Rawls • Jules, Melissa, and John O'Donnell • Julie Law • Julie Morrison • Juliet Kadar and Greg Romulus • Jussi Hölttä • Kael Spencer • Katina Montez • Kation • Kevin and Angela Myers • Kevin McCoy • Kevin Wojcik • Korben Krissy and Seth Edwards • Kristina Killgrove • Laen • Lagarto Temible • Laura Howenstine • Laurel Ladwig • Lawrence Kirkendall Leila Suri Medina • Liam & Walker Halliburton • Liam Thomas Williams • Liam, Sam, Rhiannon, Miles, Rose, Haley, Emilie, Charlotte, and Claire • Libby Bailey • Lillian and Isabel • Lily Button • Lizzie • Lois Fargo • Makoto Clark • Marianne • Mark L Sloan • Meghan Nolan Meredith Eriksen • Mia and Ken Takahashi Nieri • Mich and Giles • Michael & Samantha Mikovich • Michael and Rachelle Guerin Mike Ward • Milo and Aldis • ML Taylor • Nick • Nija Mashruwala • Norah Sisu Lenar • Owen Thompson & Stephanie Kvas • Pat Kiewicz Patrick Fjeld • Patrick Gurgel • Paul Heaberlin • Paul May • Peter E. Midford • Peter Sturdee • Phil V • Quincy Joseph Lovell Reading Evolutionary Biology Group • Rebecca Moldover • Rebecca Williams • Renata, Lila, and Talitha Blair • Rianna, Jess • Richard, Shawna, and Thomas Moraille • Robert Marshall • Roberto • Rodrigo Villaseñor Rodríguez • Roger Birkhead • Rohan and Dilan Webb Ronit, Ami, Meirav & Anat Schwab • Rui Wang • Ryan Leach • Sam Cattle • Samantha Knight • Sana Saiyed • Sandra Johnson • Sasha Siobhan Lewis • Steve and Trudee • Steve, Lori and Emily Bruun • Sue Scott • Terence, Clare & Aeryn Chua • The Bright Family The Dehgan Family • The Gardner Family • The Hess Family • The Marcus Family • The Mentzer and Twombley Family • The Roko Family Thomas and Kendall Finch • Tigger Meloy • Tilda Mills • Tim Howell • Tom Malcolm Green • Tristan A.F. Long • Uriel Minjares Vasily Maximov • Wade M Woodring • Wendy Welborn • Will & Tom Pappathan • William Howard • Xander LeRoux • Yael Notkin-Kadar Yannis Guerra • Zachary D. Wilder • Zaphod Beeblebrox • Zev Oster, Zoe Oster • Zhenya Tumanova Zoe & Brendan Jones